Quirky Wa[cky]
Children's Songs

A great collection of 11 easy-to-play songs

WISE PUBLICATIONS
part of The Music Sales Group
London/New York/Paris/Sydney/Copenhagen/Berlin/Madrid/Tokyo

995

Published by
Wise Publications
14-15 Berners Street,
London W1T 3LJ, UK.

Exclusive Distributors:
Music Sales Limited
Distribution Centre, Newmarket Road,
Bury St Edmunds, Suffolk IP33 3YB, UK.

Music Sales Pty Limited
120 Rothschild Avenue,
Rosebery, NSW 2018,
Australia.

Order No. AM987965
ISBN 1-84609-802-5
This book © Copyright 2006 by Wise Publications,
a division of Music Sales Limited.

Arrangements by Jeremy Birchall, Mark Dickman, Carl Hudson and Christopher Hussey.
Music edited by Ann Farmer.
Compiled by Nick Crispin.

Printed in the EU.

Cover photograph courtesy of iStock International Inc.

Your Guarantee of Quality
As publishers, we strive to produce every book to the highest commercial standards.
The music has been carefully designed to minimise awkward page turns and to make playing from it a real pleasure.
Particular care has been given to specifying acid-free, neutral-sized paper made from pulps
which have not been elemental chlorine bleached. This pulp is from farmed sustainable forests
and was produced with special regard for the environment.
Throughout, the printing and binding have been planned to ensure
a sturdy, attractive publication which should give years of enjoyment.
If your copy fails to meet our high standards, please inform us and
we will gladly replace it.

www.musicsales.com

The Hippopotamus Song

Words & Music by Donald Swann & Michael Flanders

1. A bold hip-po-
   fair hip-po-

(Verse 3 see block lyrics)

-pot-a-mus was stand-ing one day, on the banks of the cool Shal-i-mar.
-pot-a-ma he aimed to en-tice, from her seat on that hill-top a-bove.

He gazed at the bot-tom as he peace-full-y lay, by the light of the
As she had-n't got a ma to give her ad-vice, came tip-toe-ing

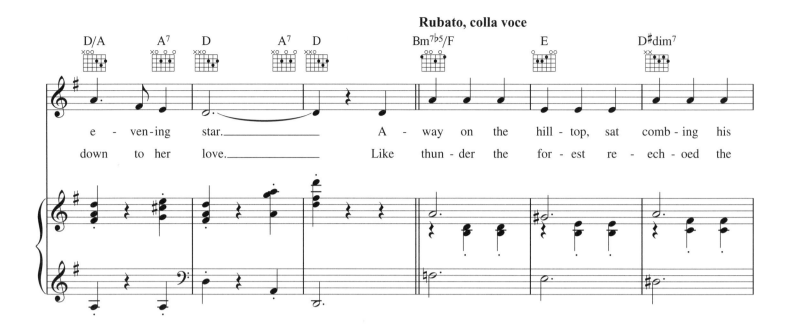

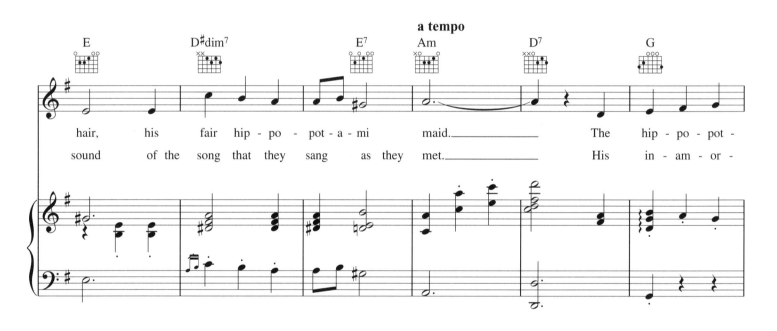

2. The glor - - i -ous

D.S. al Coda

mud. *Spoken:* That will improve our cultural relations!

3. Now,

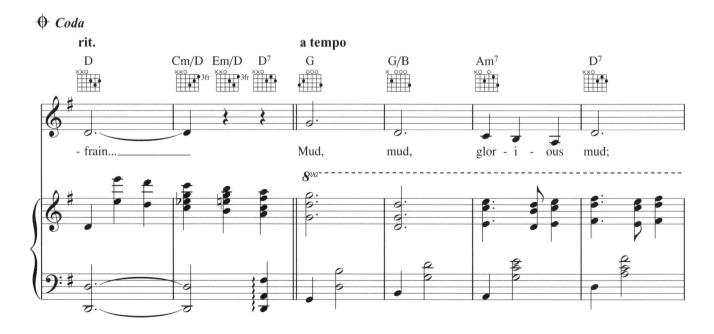

✛ *Coda*

rit.   *a tempo*

- frain..._____ Mud, mud, glor - i - ous mud;

Verse 3:

Now, more hippopotami began to convene
On the banks of that river so wide.
I wonder, now what am I to say of the scene
That ensued by the Shalimar side.
They dived all at once with an ear-splitting splosh,
Then rose to the surface again.
A regular army of hippopotami,
All singing this haunting refrain...

7

The Chicken Song

Words by Doug Naylor & Rob Grant. Music by Philip Pope

side a dog,__ and be - head an es - ki - mo. Eat a Ren - ault 4,__ wear sal - a - mi in your ears, cass - er-

-ole your gran,__ dis - em - bowel your - self with spears. The

dis - co is vib - rat - ing, the sound is loud and gra - ting, it's tru - ly naus - e - at - ing, let's do the dance a - gain.

Hold a chick - en in the air, stick a deck - chair up your nose, yes, you'll hear this song__ in your

Dry Bones

Traditional. Arranged by Livingston Gearhart

Verses 7 & 8:
Them bones them bones them dry bones *(x3)*
Now hear the word of the Lord.
[Spoken Ad Lib.] Yes Lord, Alleluia, Amen!

15

The Hokey Cokey

Words & Music by Jimmy Kennedy

* Verse 3: You put you right side in, your right side out, *etc.*

* Verse 4: You put your left leg in, your left leg out, *etc.*

* Verse 5: You put your backside in, your backside out, *etc.*

that's what it's all a - bout.
that's what it's all a - bout.

Oh_____ the Ho - key - Co - key,

oh_____ the Ho - key - Co - key,

oh_____ the Ho - key - Co - key,

1, 2.

3.

*hands clap, knees bent, yeah, yeah, yeah. You put your

yeah, yeah, yeah. You put your

* Verse 2: Get drunk, fall down, yeah, yeah, yeah.

* Verse 3: Hands up, legs straight, yeah, yeah, yeah.

* Verse 4: A ram-bam-a-loo-bam, a lam-bam-boo!

* Verse 5: Hands clap, knees bent, yeah, yeah, yeah.

Michael Finnegan

Traditional

Perpetual, at a quick pace ♩ = 120

1. There was an old man named Mi-chael Fin - ne-gan,

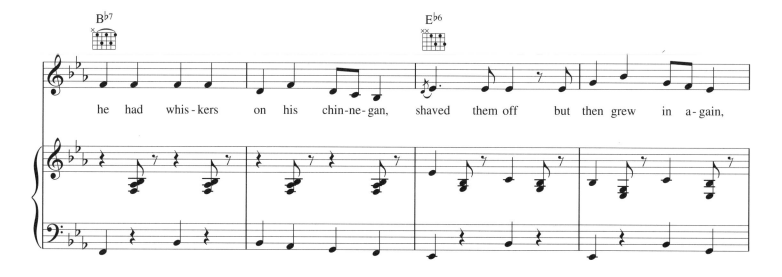

he had whis-kers on his chin-ne-gan, shaved them off but then grew in a-gain,

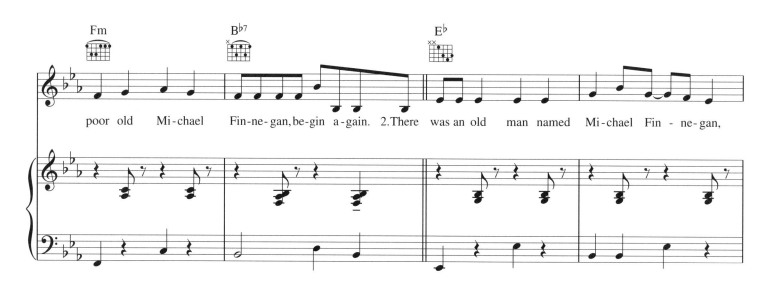

poor old Mi-chael Fin-ne-gan, be-gin a-gain. 2. There was an old man named Mi-chael Fin - ne-gan,

Monster Mash

Words & Music by Bobby Pickett & Leonard Capizzi

guests in - clu - ded__ Wolf Man, Drac - u - la, and his son. 3. The

scene was rock - ing, all were__ dig - ging_ the sounds. I - gor on chains backed by
(Verses 4 and 5 see block lyrics)

his bay - ing hounds. The Puf - fin__ Bag - gers__ were a - bout to ar - rive__ with their

vo - cal group, The Crypt Kick - er Five. They played the

Verse 2:

From my labratory in the Castle East,

To the master bedroom where the vampires feast,

The ghouls all came from their humble abodes,

To get a jolt from my electrodes.

Chorus:

They did the Mash, *etc.*

Verse 4:

Out from his coffin Drac's voice did ring,

Seems he was troubled by just one thing.

He opened the lid and shook his fist, and said,

"Whatever happened to my Transylvania Twist?"

Chorus:

It's now the Mash, *etc.*

Verse 5:

Now everything's cool, Drac's a part of the band,

And my Monster Mash is the hit of the land.

For you, the living, this Mash was meant too,

When you get to my door tell them Boris sent you.

Chorus:

Then you can Mash, *etc.*

My Old Man's A Dustman

Words & Music by Lonnie Donegan, Peter Buchanan & Beverly Thorn

A tempo ♩ = 128

My old man's a dust-man, he wears a dust-man's hat, he wears cor blim-ey trous-ers, and he

lives in a coun-cil flat. He looks a pro-per 'na - na in his great big hob-nail

boots. He's got such a job to pull them up that he calls them dais - y roots. 2. Some folks give tips at *(Verses 3, 4 & 5 see block lyrics)*

Christ-mas, and some of them_ for - get, so when he picks their bins up, he spills some on the

29

step. Now one old man got nast-y and to the coun-cil wrote; next time my old man

went round there he punched him up the throat. Oh! My old man's a dust-man, he

wears a dust-man's hat, he wears cor blim-ey trous-ers, and he lives in a coun-cil

1, 2, 3.

flat. *(Spoken interludes)* *(Vamp until ready)*

4.

flat. Next time you see a dust-man,

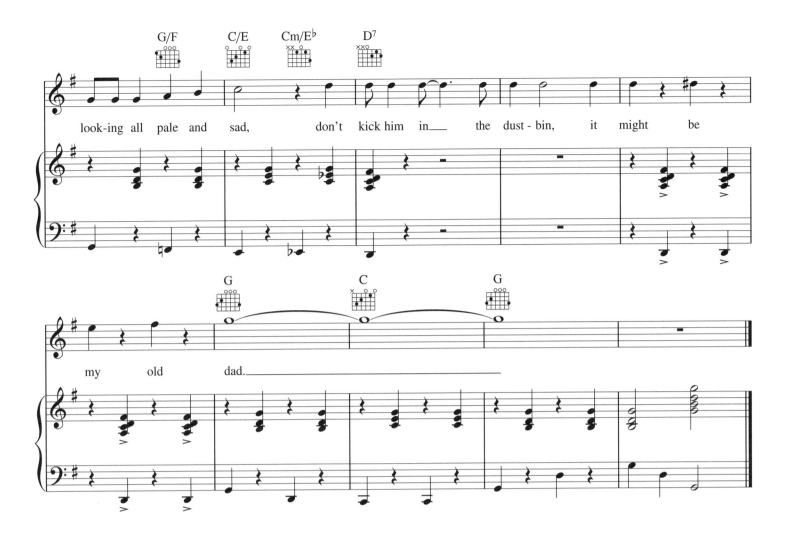

looking all pale and sad, don't kick him in the dust-bin, it might be

my old dad.

1st spoken interlude:

I say, I say, Les,

Yeah?

I found a police dog in my dustbin,

How do you know it was a police dog?

He had a policeman with him!

2nd spoken interlude:

I say, I say, I say,

Yeah?

My dustbin's full of lillies,

Well, throw them away then!

I can't; Lilly's wearing them!

3rd spoken interlude:

I say, I say, I say,

What, you again?

My dustbin's absolutely full with toadstools,

How do you know it's full?

Because there's not 'mush-room' inside!

Verse 3:

Though my old man's a dustman, he's got a heart of gold;

He got married recently, though he's eighty-six years old.

We said "Here, hang on Dad, you're getting past your prime!",

He said "Well, when you get to my age, it helps to pass the time!"

Verse 4:

Now one day in a hurry, he missed a lady's bin;

He hadn't gone but a few yards when she chased after him.

"What game do you think you're playing?", she cried right from the heart,

"You've missed, am I too late?", "No, jump up on the cart!"

Verse 5:

He found a tiger's head one day, nailed to a piece of wood;

The tiger looked quite miserable, but I suppose he should.

Just then, from out a window, a voice began to wail, he said,

"Oi, where's me tiger's head?" "Four foot from his tail!"

Nellie The Elephant

Words by Ralph Butler. Music by Peter Hart

cir - cus, off she went with a trump- e - ty trump, trump, trump, trump!

(Instrumental Break)

Three Little Fishes

Words & Music by Saxie Dowell

Light and jumpy ♩ = 75

1. Down in the mea-dow in a
2. Stop, said the mom-ma fish-y,

lit-tle bit-ty pool lived three lit-tle fish-es and a mom-ma fish-y too.
or you will get lost, but the three lit-tle fish-es did-n't want to be___ bossed. The

The Woody Woodpecker Song

Words & Music by Ramey Idriss & George Tibbles

ho - ho,　　　that's the Woo - dy Wood - peck - er's　　song.＿＿　　　He - he - he -

Right Said Fred

Words by Myles Rudge. Music by Ted Dicks

Fred said, "let's 'av a - noth - er cup o' tea", and we said, "Right - o!"
Charlie and me 'ad a - noth - er cup o' tea, and then we went

2."Al - 'ome!

Vamp until ready

Spoken: I said to Charlie, "We'll just 'ave to leave it standin' on the landin',
that's all. You see the trouble with Fred is, 'e's...'e's too 'asty.
Now, you never get nowhere if you're too 'asty!"

1 2 3 4 5 6 7 8 9